Color Your Soul

Outside the lines..

by Vendula Kalinova

COLOR YOUR SOUL

OUTSIDE THE LINES..

SOUL MEDITATIVE SERIES

- VOLUME 1 -

Artist's Mandala Meditative Poetry Coloring book

ISBN: 9780578352817 (PAPERBACK)
LIBRARY OF CONGRESS CONTROL NUMBER: 2021924988

2ND EDITION - JANUARY, 2022
NEW YORK, NEW YORK
@KALINOVADESIGN

COVER ART & BOOK DESIGN BY VENDULA KALINOVA
COVER CHAKRA STONE ELEMENT ©DEBRA CARR /COVER WATERCOLOR TEXTURE ©AGA7TA / INTERIOR WATERCOLOR BACKGROUND ©RUDCHENKO VIA CANVA.COM

Dedication

To the sunshine in my life
To the prettiest flower within my garden
To the pillar of my strength
To you Gabby Gonzalez
a beautiful daughter
I solely dedicate my creation
for it would not become without you...

"DIVE INTO A SPIRITUAL JOURNEY, WHERE YOU WILL EXPLORE BEAUTIFUL PATTERNS
OF YOUR SUBCONSCIOUS MIND.
THIS BOOK WILL GUIDE YOU TO OVERTAKE A NEW INNER PATH THAT LEADS TO HIDDEN TREASURES.
VENDULA HAS A UNIQUE MAGICAL TOUCH OF TRANSFORMING EMOTIONS INTO A WORK OF ART."

-AFAF KHALIL, VISUAL ARTIST/DESIGNER, AND CREATIVE EDUCATOR
WWW.AFAFKHALIL.COM

"I HAVE MET VENDULA IN AN ACADEMIC SETTING. GETTING TO KNOW HER THROUGH HER WORK ASSURED ME
THAT SHE WAS ALREADY BORN AN ARTIST, AND THUS HAD NOT TO LEARN HOW TO BECOME ONE.
BEING BORN AN ARTIST IS ACKNOWLEDGING A GIFT (WE ALL HAVE) AND NATURALLY ALLOWING IT TO BE DEPICTED
IN THE AND THROUGH THE ARTIST'S WORK, EFFORTLESSLY.
ART JUST FLOWS THROUGH VENDULA'S HANDS, INTUITIVELY GUIDED BY HER DEEP INNER INTENTION
OF MANIFESTING LIFE THROUGH ART.
THIS GESTURE OF SHARING LIFE—AN INVITATION FOR US TO LIVE LIFE AT ITS FULLEST —IS LATENT
IN EACH OF VENDULA'S MANDALAS, AWAITING TO BE LIVED THROUGH THE COLOR PALETTE EACH ONE OF US CHOOSES. "

-MARCIA LOPES DE MELLO,
AN ARCHITECT AND EDUCATOR BY PROFESSION, AND AN ART LOVER BY HEART AND SOUL

"I LIVED VICARIOUSLY THROUGH VENDULA'S ART.
HER AFFIRMATIONS SWAYED ME TO CONFRONT THE OVERWHELMING SENSATION
OF TRANQUILITY BETWEEN MIND, BODY, AND SOUL.
WHILE I READ AND COLORED, I BELIEVED THE ARTIST AND I SHARED A SECRET LANGUAGE."

-ANA MARTINEZ, ASPIRING WRITER

"VENDULA'S ARTWORK AND POEMS AT ONCE EVOKE A SENSE OF SERENITY AND PEACE IN THE VIEWER.
SYMMETRY, HARMONY AND BEAUTY SEEK EXPRESSION THROUGH ART TO UPLIFT AND TRANSFORM LIFE
INTO A FULLER AND MORE MEANINGFUL EXPERIENCE.
WHILE FOR MANY ARTISTS THIS MAY BE THE OBJECTIVE, VENDULA SEEMS TO START RIGHT AT THIS HIGH POINT GOAL
AND WORK OUTWARD TO TOUCH AND INSPIRE ONE TO AN INNER JOURNEY OF SELF DISCOVERY."

-JOSEPH BALINT, PHOTOGRAPHER
@JOEBALINTMUSIC

"THROUGH ENGAGING WITH VENDULA'S ARTWORK, ONE CAN ALLOW THE MIND
TO MORE FULLY ABSORB THE INSPIRING AFFIRMATIONS. EMBARK ON A JOURNEY
OF CREATIVITY AND DISCOVERY WITH A NEW SENSE OF WONDER AT THE TURN OF EACH PAGE.
THE IMAGES AND POEMS CREATE A BEAUTIFUL BALANCE OF GROUNDING AND ELEVATION."

-TODD DIERINGER, OWNER/ARTIST AT NICOLAS TOD DESIGNS
WWW.NICOLASTODDESIGNS.COM

"Nulla dies sine linea.."

– Pliny the Elder

Table of Contents

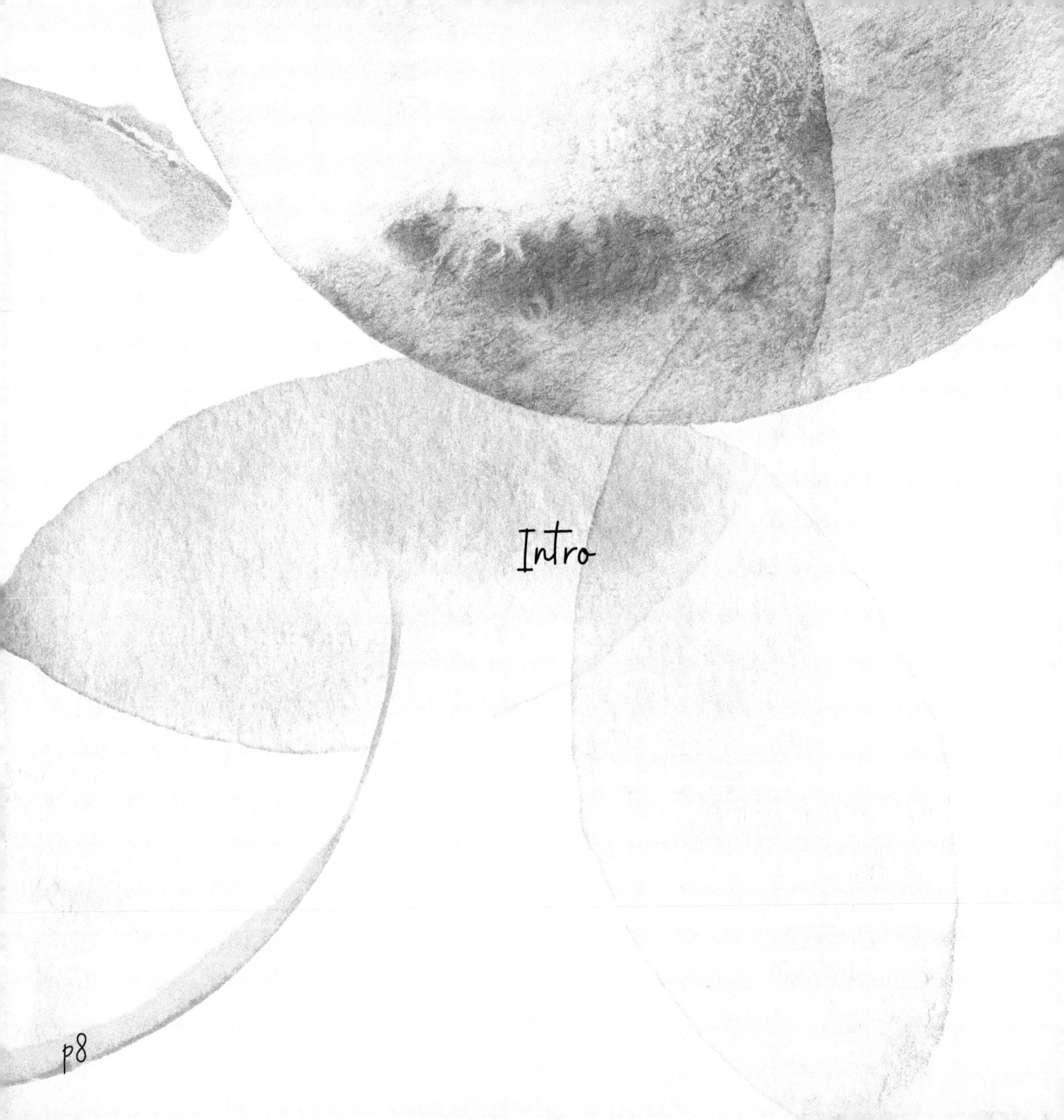

Intro

"Color Your Soul" is a meditative collection
of one-of-a-kind mandalas that are meant to bring
the joy of mindfulness into your spiritual practice.
Allow your focus to ground you, and engage your creativity with coloring.

The Artist Vendula Kalinova has created 33 Buddhist hand-drawn illustrations
accompanied by 33 healing poem affirmations,
to inspire you on a creative and calming journey.
Immerse yourself in the positive energy of self-care,
and awaken your artistic vision by coloring wherever your intuition takes you.
Outside the lines and spirit-free; allow yourself to relax, re-center,
and freely enjoy the beauty
of Spirituality, Art & Poetry in your own masterpiece.

Letter from the Artist

There is power in creating something
inspired by your intuition..
For intentionally I look at the world through the lens of beauty
and create a deeper sense of understanding for this silent guidance.
I have unwavering faith and gratitude for the gift of this inner voice,
and the magic that transcends when I listen.
This book is no short of being a blessing of the divine guidance it was created in.
In many sunsets on my rooftop and many nights lasting till dawn, I placed
my energy into manifesting this book into its birth, and now into your hands.
I hope it will bring some uninterrupted moments of serenity your way
as much as it did to me while creating it.

With Love & Light
~ Vendula Kalinova

Set some time away

Sit in a quiet place

Reflect in gratitude

Choose words that call on you

Journal, color away

& let your energy pour onto the pages..

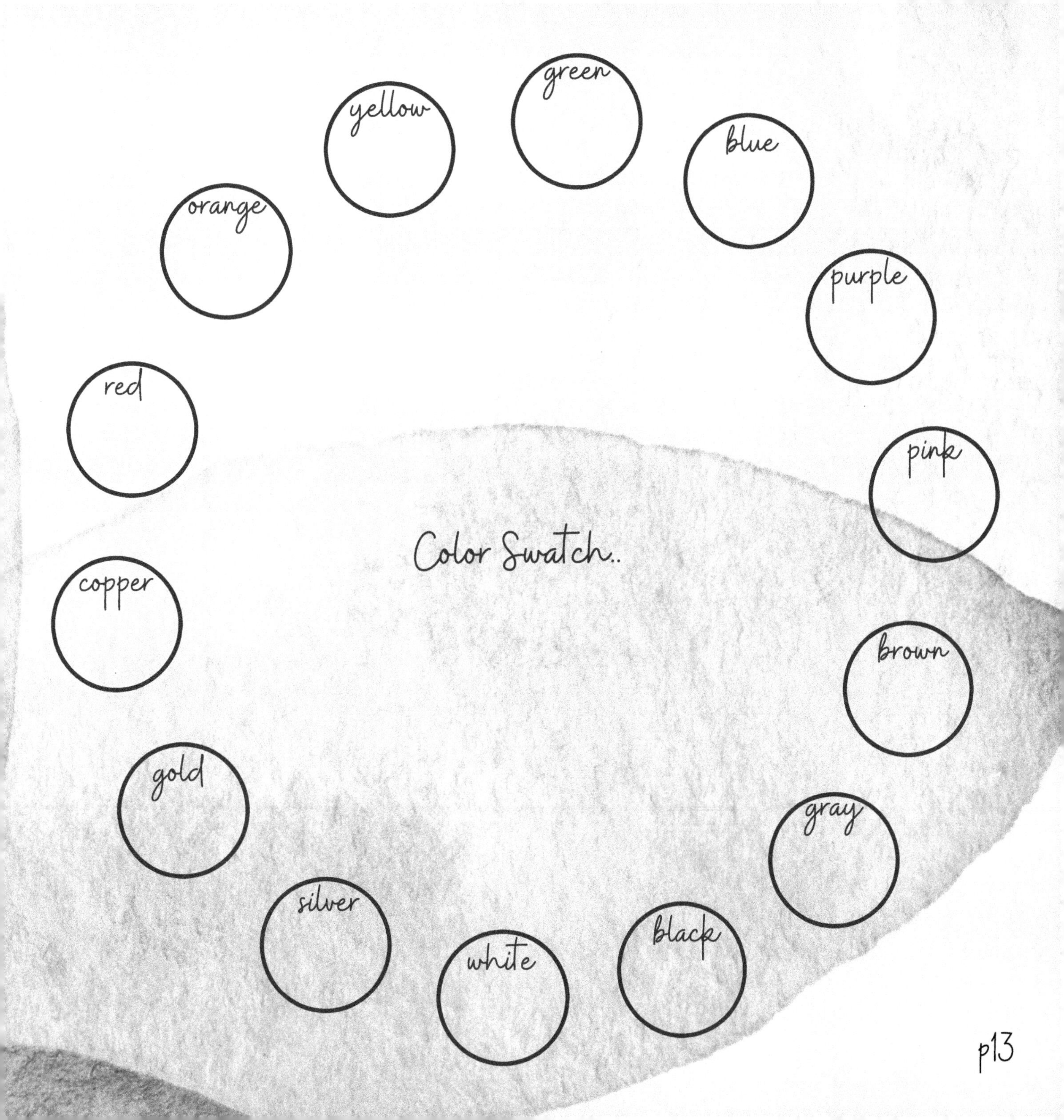
green
yellow
blue
orange
purple
red
pink
Color Swatch..
copper
brown
gold
gray
silver
black
white

pages 20-41

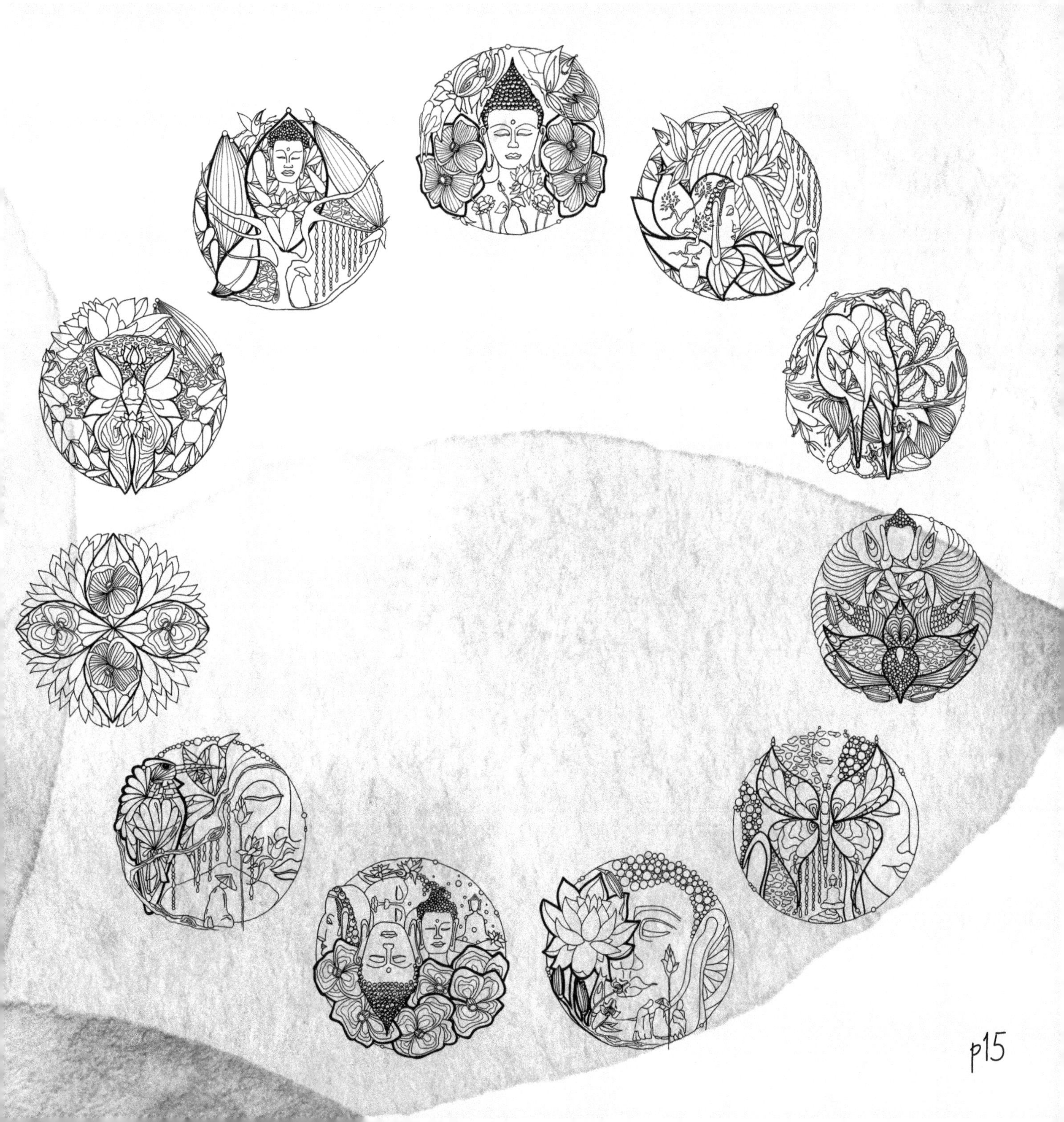

pages 42-63

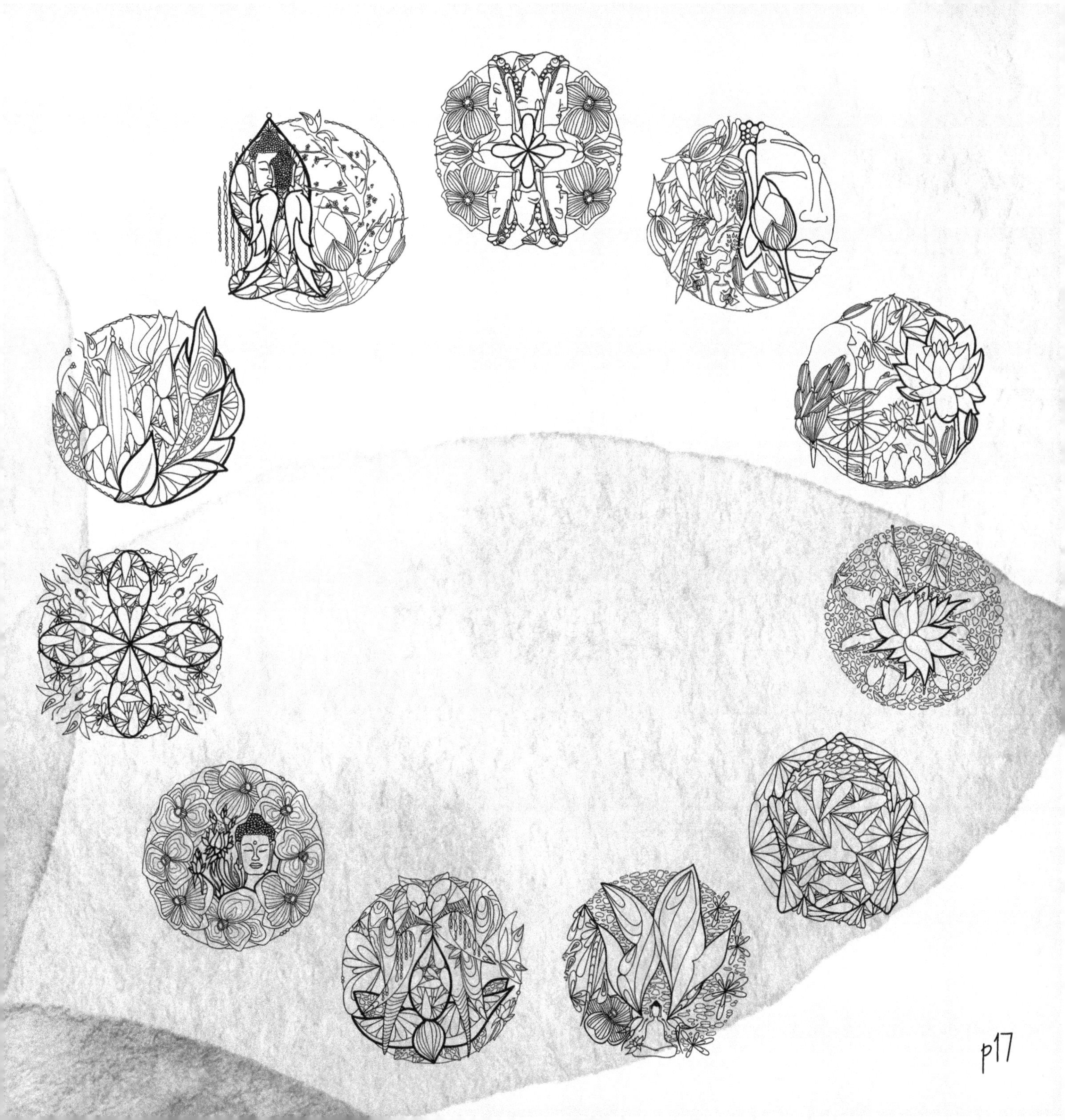

pages 64-85

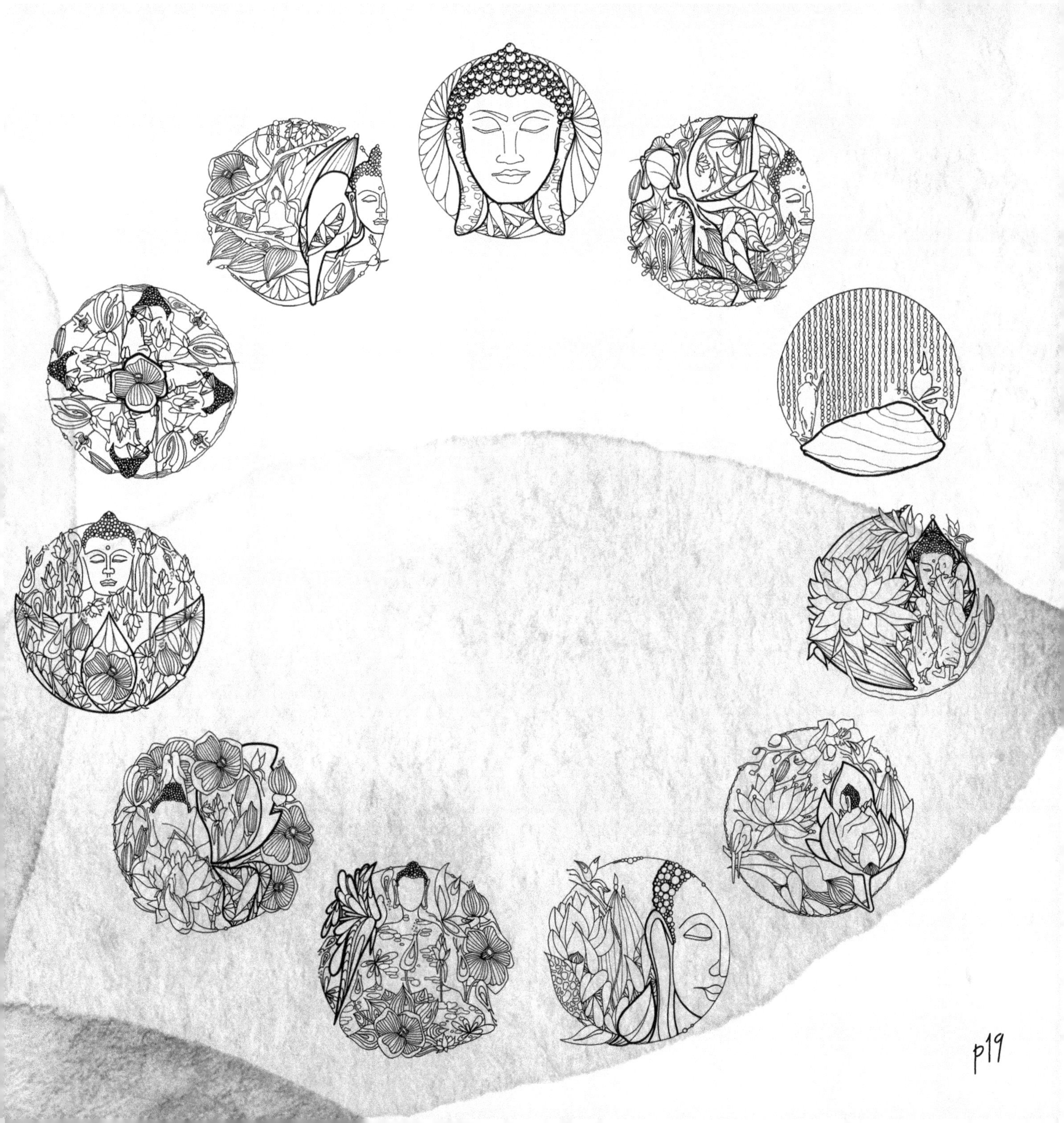

Where ever that is..

I find myself here

In this precise moment

I am here and now

I am present

In the grace of my potential
divine purpose reveals..
With kindness and patience
my soul therefore heals
I choose myself
for I am worthy

Each day I am willing to let go of
what no longer serves me
Each day I am open to change
Each day my mind transcends..
For eternally I am healing my wounds

There is a temple
Fleeting thus omnipotent
and that of my body
It speaks to me and I listen fondly
I care for it well, with and without..
For eternally I am healthy

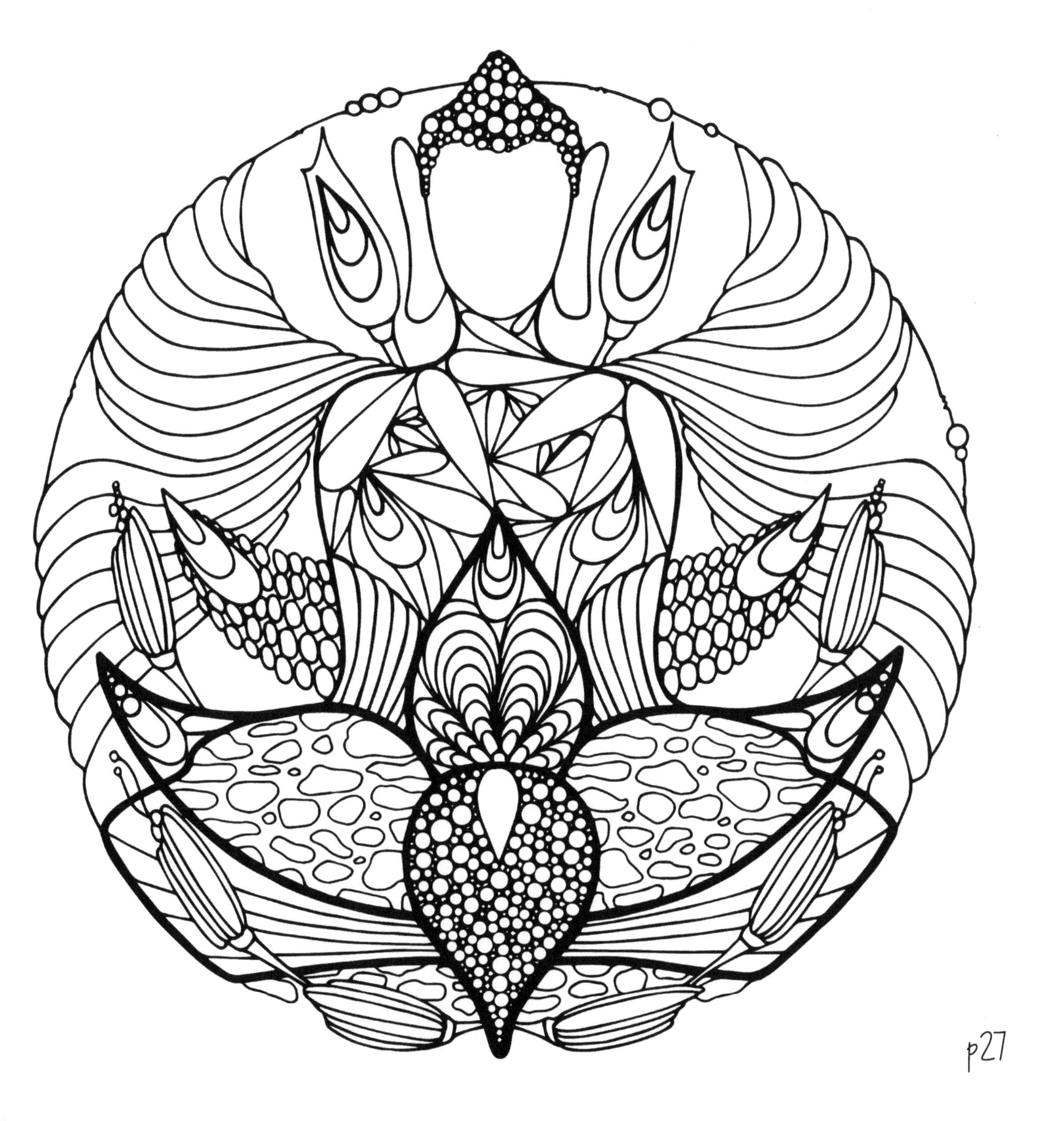

I foster my mind

I nourish my body

I nurture my soul

I cherish my instrument

The song of abundance there plays..

My thoughts create my world
Earnestly I choose to observe them so
The shiny reflection bestows upon me
thoughts that nourish and support me
will inspire me so..

In times of hardship

there I meditate into calmness

I breathe

I am in peace..

With intent I create

I allow and receive

I accept myself as I am

in this very moment..

I protect my self-worth

I merit my precious energy

I enter the sacred path to a higher self

With each day

my moral compass strengthens..

In humility and respect

I interrelate with those around me

In awareness I govern my emotions

With integrity I hold the firmness of my word

Each day I assure I gracefully rest
I affirm I sleep well and awaken refreshed
I am looking forward to each and new day
For new experiences enter my way..

I release, and let go of resistance

I pay no heed to the past

I let go of pain with forgiveness

" Quest to seek within "

the soul asks..

Create a new way of thinking

For your energy will be cleansed

I have a smile on my face

In high resonance I dance..

Through a creative self-expression

only positive energy stands a chance

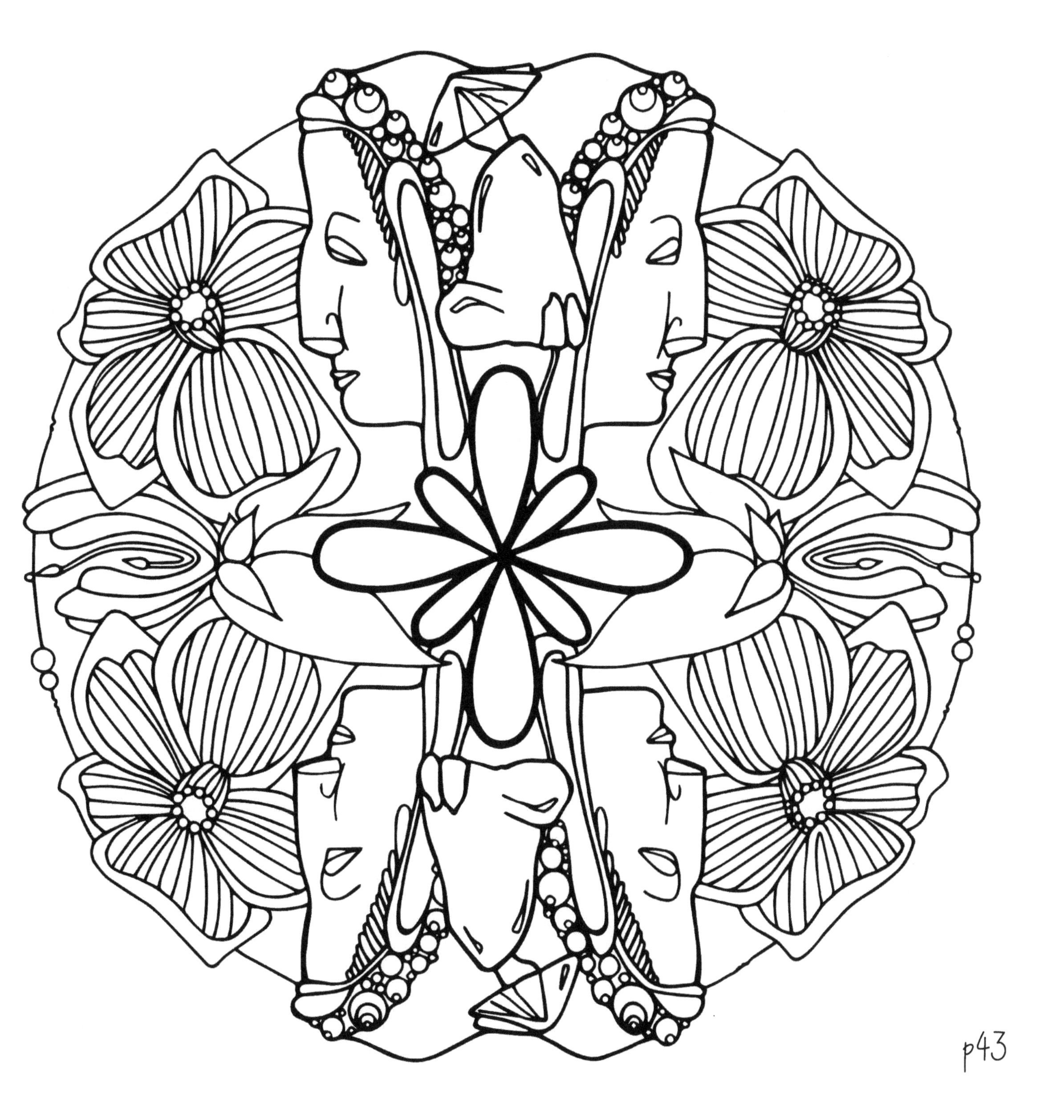

My smile is contagious

My innate nature of authentic self

raises the vibration of this world

For I can heal those who fall

uplifting their tender spirit..

Each day I take time to learn
It is the pursuit of knowledge
what adorns my soul
In virtue of my self-growth
I watch my progress in delight
In here and now I pay forward
and illuminate to ignite..

I allow thoughts to pass freely

No sail into the wind

no gravity needed to reserve..

I allow the Universe to work through me

What serves me will come my way

My words carry power..

In wisdom I speak

In a poem of existence I glisten

Serenity is what I seek

With patience I listen

for clarity is always near

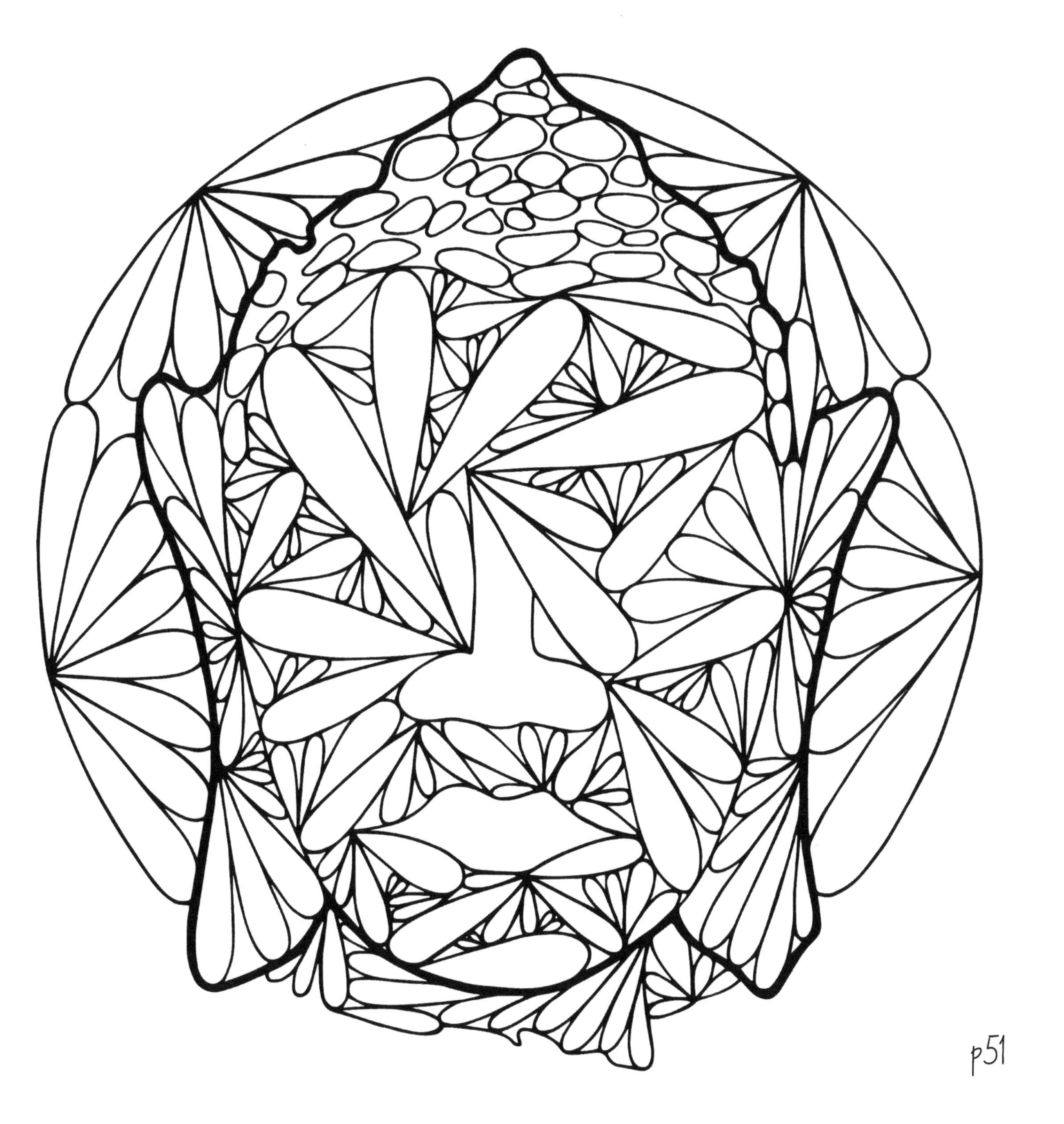

My actions convey compassion

My heart opens to all

I seek to share knowledge

As summer seeks the fall..

I seek to land a hand

In a bountiful way I grant

With positive energy I lead

With permission I believe

Cleansing energy washes over me

In guidance I travel

The road to divinity appears..

I Dream BIG

So big.. others at times may not understand

Welcome, I say..

Even more so I believe

with unwavering faith

I draw success towards me

I am inspired into action
for desire burns within my path..
With an abundant mind I choose to create
Each step aligns with my vision
therefore each day I move toward my dream

Each day I wake with excitement

As the past fades away

the future finds its way..

With each day I gain momentum

My deeds align with the greater good

My results echo my ardent efforts

p61

Passion is what burns within me

Toward my dreams I travel so..

My ideal self

I dare to know

The solace in knowing

is where the new will be born

My greater purpose reveals itself to me
For the highest good of all
The instrument of my talents
will deliver in awe..

In solemn promise I pledge to give
In blessed energy therefore I live

My soul is enchanted with life
Life of passion, love, health, and joy
I deserve the very best
I am willing to lovingly accept and receive
I live effortlessly
In peace and harmony I transcend..

I smile, I laugh, I am joyful

I pay attention to signs around me..

I listen to my inner voice

I trust the divine guidance within me

I feel protected and loved

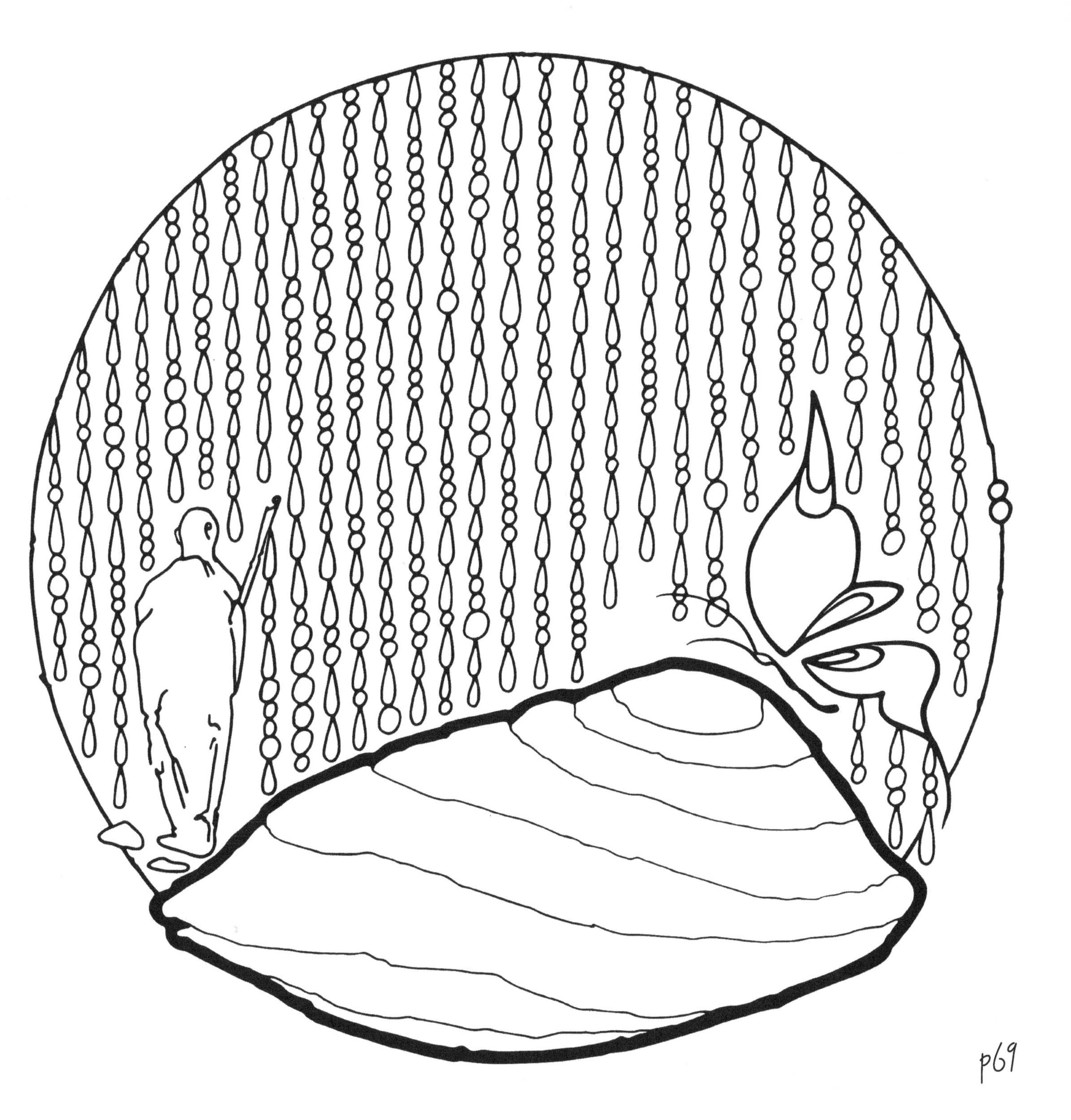

My soul is filled with inspiration

and my creativity flows seamlessly

I inhale the divine and exhale my gratitude

I manifest the beauty created within me

In prosperity I receive..

With generosity I give

With peace I exist
In health I stand
With strength I walk
In resilience I learn
With kindness I share..

With compassion I serve

With conviction I intend

With prowess I create

With patience I await

With appreciation I receive..

I am deeply connected to my intuition

I carry myself with grace

I follow my dreams

Boundless my mind remains

In limitless ways I expand..

I am connected to the higher power

I see myself from above..

I see my potential

I believe in myself

The light is within me

I am kind and compassionate
to myself and to others
I respect nature and all its creatures
Love washes over me
with all that surrounds me..

Positive energy, the dearest of friends
allows a gift my way
The gift of an open heart
For my energy can embrace those in need
as divine energy enters through my being..

With energy I inspire

In awe of this life I feel

In prayer I meditate

With gratitude I lead

Towards light I travel so..

p85

Reflection Notes

Acknowledgements

I would like to say Thank You to a few special people
who have contributed to the making of this creation...
to Gabby Gonzalez for the behind the scenes, support, critiques, laughs,
encouragements, and many "no's" that edited this piece into what it became.
To a Dear friend Laszlo Huve for introducing me to the path of inner peace
and for being the kindest of souls.
to my peers; whose work I very much so admire, who have taken the time
to review this book and kidly given an endorsement for my work.
To my Mentor, Professor, and Dear friend Marcia Lopes De Mello who has
embedded design principles into my practice, and paved the way for my vision to be.
To Joseph Balint for his creative input, expertise, and ongoing support.
To Ana Martinez, the young lady whose potential is brighter than the sun,
and whose written words are being awaited by this world!
To Todd Dieringer who captures unseen details missed by many
in every flower there is...
...... and to Afaf Khalil, my Dearest of Art friends
whose Art, soul & heart inspires me
to the moon and back!

REFERENCES:

PLINY THE ELDER, HISTORIA NATURALIS; XXXV/84

Biography

Vendula Kalinova is a New York-based Visual Artist,
originating from the roots of Czech Republic.
She has created a multidimensional body of work from Fashion, to Visual Arts,
Sculptures, and much in between. Vendula's work not only resembles her passion
for working with hands but as a trained Designer in several fields,
allowing her to blend her Design skills with Art.
The core of her inspiration is highly interlaced with her spiritual journey;
through which she explores the depths of Art and the limitless boundaries
of her innate expression.
While her work encompasses a variety of disciplines; her focus
for the past several years has been intuitive Art
combined with Spirituality, Meditation, and Poetry.

Please tag your colored masterpiece
& spread the inspiration!

Thank you for allowing me

to connect with you through my Art.

May your journey be blessed..

.... and may your light shine bright!

Love

~Vendula

CPSIA information can be obtained
at www.ICGtesting.com
Printed in the USA
LVHW071329140122
708505LV00009B/290